我和月亮一起散步
I Took the Moon for a Walk

Written by Carolyn Curtis
Illustrated by Alison Jay

Simplified Chinese translation by Fang Wang

Mantra Lingua

I took the Moon for a walk last night.
It followed behind like a still summer kite,

昨夜我和月亮一起散步了。
月亮就像一只大风筝似的跟在我的身后。

Though there wasn't a string or a tail in sight
when I took the Moon for a walk.

尽管没有任何线牵着月亮。
当我和月亮一起散步的时候。

I carried my blue torch just in case
the Moon got scared and hid its face.

我还带着我的蓝色手电筒以防万一，
月亮却被吓得藏起了它的脸，

但是月亮却透过淡淡的云朵偷偷地注视着我。
当我和月亮一起散步的时候，

But it peeked through clouds
that were fragile as lace
When I took the Moon for a walk.

I warned the Moon to rise a bit higher
so it wouldn't get hooked on a church's tall spire,

我告诉月亮要升起得高一点，
这样月亮就不会被教堂尖尖的屋顶钩住了。

While the neighbourhood dogs made a train-whistle choir
when I took the Moon for a walk.

邻居家的狗的叫声像火车的汽笛一样。
当我和月亮一起散步的时候，

We tiptoed through grass where the night crawlers creep
when the rust-bellied robins have all gone to sleep,

我们小心翼翼地踮着脚走过小昆虫们睡觉的草丛。
当所有红腹知更鸟都去睡觉的时候，

月亮叫来了一滴滴像眼泪似的露珠落在青草上。
当我和月亮一起散步的时候，

And the Moon called the dew so the grass seemed to weep
When I took the Moon for a walk.

我们比赛荡秋千，看看谁的脚更高，
我还想象着月亮
是如何叫我像它一样飞起来。

We raced for the swings,
where I kicked my feet high
And imagined the Moon had
just asked me to fly,

Hand holding hand through the starry night sky
when I took the Moon for a walk.

我们手拉着手飞过布满星星的夜空。
当我和月亮一起散步的时候，

We danced 'cross the bridge where the smooth waters flow.
The Moon was above and the Moon was below,

我们跳着舞穿过了静静流淌的小河，穿过了小桥。
月亮高悬在天空，美丽的剪影倒映在水中。

柔和的月光笼罩着我的全身，
当我和月亮一起散步的时候。

And bright in between them
I echoed in their glow
When I took the Moon for a walk.

Then as we turned back, the Moon kept me in sight.
It followed me home and stayed there all night,

当我们回去的时候，月亮一直都静静地陪在我的左右。
月亮和我回到了家中，整晚不曾离去。

And thanked me by sharing its sweet sleepy light
when I took the Moon for a walk.

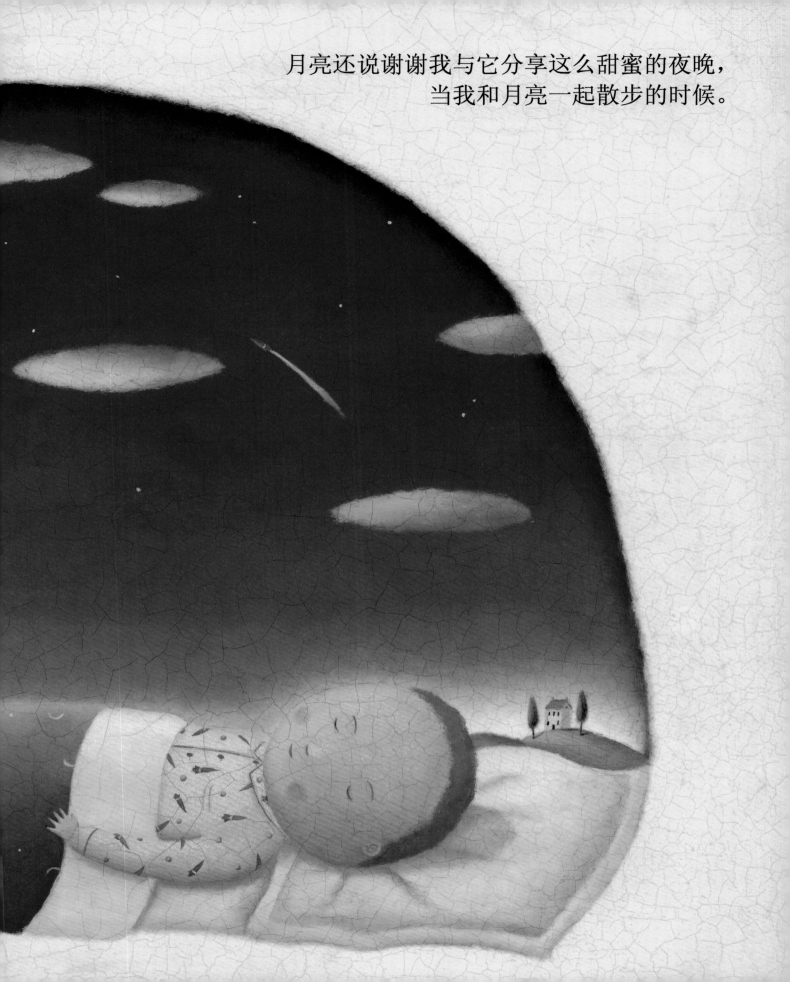

月亮还说谢谢我与它分享这么甜蜜的夜晚，
当我和月亮一起散步的时候。

The Mysterious Moon

What do you see when you look at the moon? Children who live in Europe and the United States imagine that they see a man when they look at the moon. Children in Japan and India see a rabbit, and children in Australia see a kitten. But all children, no matter where they live, look up in wonder at the same moon.

The moon is primarily made of rock with a small iron core. It creates no light of its own, but reflects sunlight.

The shape of the moon seems to change during the month because the sunlight strikes the moon at different angles as it travels through space. These shapes are called 'phases'. Here are some of the phases of the moon:

New Moon   Crescent Moon   Half Moon   Gibbous Moon   Full Moon

When the moon is growing larger in the sky, we say that it is 'waxing'. When it is growing smaller, we say that it is 'waning'.

For people all over the world, the moon has always been an important way to measure time. Although the solar calendar has become the standard international way of doing this, many people still use lunar, or moon, calendars.

The moon can be a friend to farmers and gardeners - those who follow tradition know that the best time to sow seeds and transplant young shoots is when the moon is waxing.

Moon festivals are celebrated in many societies. The Chinese Moon Festival is held during the Harvest Moon - the full moon that rises in mid-autumn.

Many Celtic and Native American festivals are also held at the time of the Harvest Moon, when the people give thanks for the harvest and for all living things on earth.

The World at Night

If you took the moon for a walk through your neighbourhood, what would you show it? What would you hear, and what would you see?

Wherever you are, you would probably see some nocturnal creatures - mammals, birds and insects that usually sleep during the day and come out at night. They are especially adapted to life under the moon and stars:

Cats have eyes that see very well in the dark.

Rabbits have large ears that capture sound across long distances.

Bats use sounds and echoes to help them fly safely and find food.

Fireflies light up at night so that they can find each other.

Owls have necks that can turn right around and huge, flat eyes that enable them to see other creatures that are far away.

Some flowers are nocturnal too. They bloom and release their fragrance after dark.

And although you are asleep during the night, your mind is not! During the day, your waking, or conscious, mind is active, but when you sleep, your dreaming, or unconscious, mind is busy. So, the world at night is not so quiet as it seems!

For my nephew Christopher, *who first walked with the moon*
and my mother Estella, *who held his hand*
For my father Harold, *the star we steer by*
and Lucan, *my sun*
and, of course, for Emilie, *for Everything* - C.C.

The author extends heartfelt thanks to the society of Children's Book Writers and Illustrators for generous support in the form of
a Barbara Karlin Grant, WarmLines Parent Resources, Jane Yolen, the Jeff Kelly and Newton Library Critique Groups, and Alison Keehn.

For Mark, happy moon walking, love from Alison.

Mantra Lingua TalkingPEN
Global House
303 Ballards Lane
London N12 8NP
www.mantralingua.com
www.talkingpen.co.uk

First published in Great Britain in 2004 by Barefoot Books Ltd
Dual language edition first published 2008 by Mantra Lingua
This edition 2019

Printed in Letchworth, UK. PE200519PB06193871

A CIP record of this book is available from the British Library